THE BEST OF CHRISTMAS

Complete Words and Music

80 GREAT SONGS FOR THE HOLIDAY SEASON

arranged for PIANO, VOCAL and GUITAR

ISBN: 0 8494 0132 1

40640

THE BEST OF CHRISTMAS

80 Great Songs For The Holiday Season

THE BEST OF CHRISTMAS

80 Great Songs For The Holiday Season

7678

©HVAS

ANGELS FROM THE REALMS OF GLORY

J. MONTGOMERY
H. SMART

40640

ALL AROUND THE CHRISTMAS TREE

By
SUNNY SKYLAR and
SAMMY KAYE

Moderato, Not Too Slowly

ALL A-ROUND THE CHRIST-MAS TREE, the Christ-mas tree, the Christ-mas tree;

ALL A-ROUND THE CHRIST-MAS TREE on mer-ry Christ-mas day.

Pre-sents all a-round the tree, the Christ-mas tree, the Christ-mas tree;

Pre-sents all a-round the tree so bright and new and gay.

There's a
There's a
Hear the

pret - ty blue dress for Moth - er and the doll for sis - ter Sue, There's a
bon - net for Aunt Mi - rand - y, there's a tie for Un - cle Jim and the
jin - gle bells ting - a - ling - in', Christ - mas time is here a - gain and the

beau - ti - ful bike for broth - er and a watch for Dad - dy too, Oh,
stock - ings are filled with cand - y, some for me and cou - sin Tim, Oh,
choir___ is soft - ly sing - in' "Peace on Earth, Good Will Toward Men," Oh,

ALL A-ROUND THE CHRIST-MAS TREE, the Christ-mas tree, the Christ-mas tree;

ALL A-ROUND THE CHRIST-MAS TREE on mer - ry Christ-mas day. day.

3

ALL I WANT FOR CHRISTMAS IS MY TWO FRONT TEETH

Words and Music by
DON GARDNER

Gee, if I could on-ly have my two front teeth, then I could wish you, "Mer-ry Christ-mas" It

seems so long since I could say, "Sis-ter Su-sie sit-ting on a this-tle!"

Gosh oh gee, how hap-py I'd be, if I could on-ly whis-tle (thhh.) All I want for Christ-mas is MY

TWO FRONT TEETH, my two front teeth, see my two front teeth. Gee, if I could on-ly have my

two front teeth, then I could wish you "Mer-ry Christ-mas!" I could wish you "Mer-ry Christ-mas!"

ALL THROUGH THE NIGHT

By
NICK REYNOLDS

ANGELS WE HAVE HEARD ON HIGH

TRADITIONAL

1. An - gels we have heard on high, sweet - ly sing - ing
2. Shep - herds, why this ju - bi - lee? Why your joy - ous

o'er the plains, And the moun - tains in re - ply,
strains pro - long? What the glad - some tid - ings be

ech - o - ing their joy - ous strains. Glo -
which in - spire your joy heav - 'n'ly song?

3. Come to Bethlehem and see
   Him whose birth the angels sing.
   Come, adore on bended knee
   Christ the Lord, the newborn King,
   Gloria in excelsis Deo.
   Gloria in excelsis Deo.

4. See Him in a manger laid,
   Whom the choirs of angels praise,
   Mary, Joseph, lend your aid,
   While our hearts in love we raise.
   Gloria in excelsis Deo.
   Gloria in excelsis Deo.

ARE MY EARS ON STRAIGHT?

Moderato *(lightly)*

Words and Music by
MEL LEVEN

AS JOSEPH WAS A-WALKING

rocked to sleep In a cra - dle trimmed with gold, But in the wood - en man - ger That li - eth in the mold. As Jo - seph was a - walk - ing Thus did the an - gel sing And Ma - ry's Son at mid - night Was born to be our King. Then be you glad, good peo - ple, At this time of the year And light you up your can - dles For His star shin - eth clear.

AWAY IN A MANGER

MARTIN LUTHER
J. E. SPILLMAN

14

O SANCTISSIMA

SICILIAN FOLK SONG

Moderato

Day of ho-li-ness, peace and hap-pi-ness, Joy-ful, glo-ri-ous Christ-mas day!

An-gels tell the sto-ry of this day of glo-ry. Praise Christ, our Sav-iour, born this Christ-mas day!

THE BELLS OF ST. MARY'S

Words by DOUGLAS FURBER
Music by A. EMMETT ADAMS

Moderato

The bells of St. Ma-ry's at sweet ev-en-tide, Shall
At the porch of St. Ma-ry's I'll wait there {with}{for} you In {your}{my}

call me be-lov-éd, to come to your side, And out in the val-ley in
soft wed-ding dress with its rib-bons of blue, In the church of St. Ma-ry's sweet

sound of the sea, I know you'll be wait-ing, yes wait-ing for me. The
voi - ces shall sing, For you and me dear-est the wed-ding bells ring.

Refrain

Bells of St. Ma - ry's, Ah! hear they are call - ing The

young loves— the true loves Who come from the sea, And

so my be - lov - éd, When red leaves are fall - ing, The

love-bells shall ring out— ring out For you and me. The

Bells of St. Ma - ry's, Ah! hear they are call - ing The

18

young loves — the true loves Who come from the sea, And so, my be-

lov-éd, When red leaves are fall-ing, The love-bells shall ring out — ring out For

you and me. you and me.

THE BIRTHDAY OF A KING

WILLIAM HOWARD NEIDLINGER

20

lu - ia, how it rang! And the sky____ was bright with a

ho - ly light; 'Twas the birth-day of a King!

'Twas a King!

21

BE A SANTA

Words by
BETTY COMDEN
and ADOLPH GREEN
Music by JULE STYNE

What you bring - 'll fill the world with joy. Come on and twink that twin - kle, Wrin - kle your eyes, Wob - ble your chins, Ring out your bell. Re - mem - ber wink and gig - gle, Wig - gle your beard, Keep up your

2nd time to Coda

grins, Get out and sell the spell of old No - el, No - el! Oh!

Be a San - ta, Ro - ly San - ta, Po - ly

San - ta, Spread the word of Mer - ry Christ - mas. Be so jol - ly,

Decked with hol - ly, And by gol - ly, Ev - 'ry - one will

24

love you if you'll be a San - ta Claus. ___

Grab your bel - ly, then let go. Shake like jel - ly, to and fro.

8va (if desired)

mp

Ha, ha, ha, ha, ha, ha, ha, ha! Ho, ho, ho, ho, ho, ho, ho, ho!

Roar and bel - low in the snow, Like a mel - low buf - fa - lo. Ha, ha, ha, ha,

THE CHRISTMAS SONG
(Chestnuts Roasting On An Open Fire)

Lyric by MEL TORME
Music by ROBERT WELLS

mos. Ev - 'ry - bod - y   find it hard to sleep   to - night.   They know that

San   -   ta's on his   way;   He's load - ed   lots of toys and good - ies on his

sleigh.   And ev - 'ry   moth - er's child ____ is gon - na   spy ____ to see if

rein-deer_ real-ly know how to fly. And so, I'm of-fer-ing this

sim-ple phrase to kids from one to nine-ty-two. Al-

tho' it's been said man-y times, man-y ways; "Mer-ry Christ-mas to you."

rit.

CAROL OF THE BELLS

Ukranian Carol
M. LEONTOVICH

A CAROLING WE GO

By JOHNNY MARKS

Moderately Bright

1. A car - ol - ing, a car - ol - ing, a
2. (We) bring you sea - son's greet - ings and we
   (More slowly)
3. (Now) you may have your hol - ly and per -
   (a tempo - slowly fade to end)
4. (A) car - ol - ing, a car - ol - ing, a

car - ol - ing we go, Hearts filled with mu - sic and
wish the best to you, And may our wish last the
haps some mis - tle - toe, May - be a fir tree and
car - ol - ing we go, Hearts filled with mu - sic and

CHRISTMAS IN KILLARNEY

Words and Music by
JOHN REDMOND
JAMES CAVANAUGH
and FRANK WELDON

COVENTRY CAROL

ENGLISH TRADITIONAL

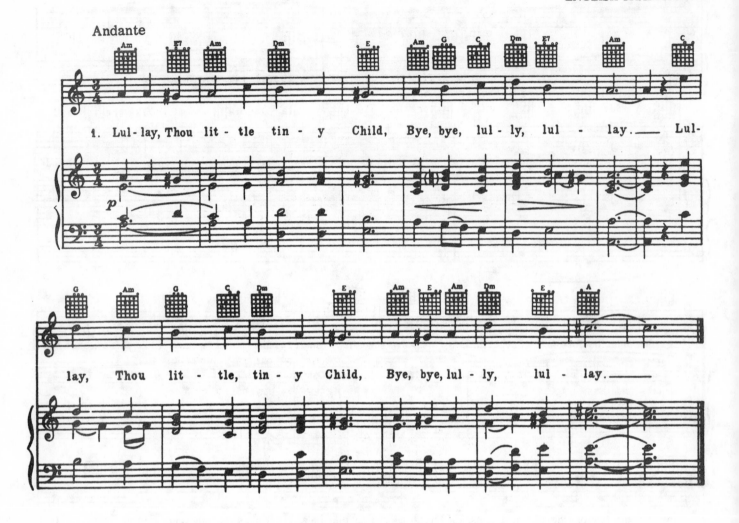

2. O sisters, too,
How may we do
For to preserve this day?
This poor Youngling
For whom we sing
Bye, bye, lully, lullay.

3. Then woe is me,
Poor Child, for Thee,
And ever mourn and say
For Thy parting,
Nor say, nor sing
Bye, bye, lully, lullay.

DECK THE HALLS

WELSH TRADITIONAL

EVERY CHRISTMAS MORNING

Words and Music by
BOB GODFREY, "CY" GILLIS
and BILL WEEKS

39

When I spy my pres - ents ___ be - neath the Christ - mas tree

I get so ex - cit - ed, hap - py as can be.

Ev - 'ry Christ - mas morn - ing ___ I'm glad that I was born ___ So

I can get that feel - ing ___ that comes on Christ - mas morn.

comes on Christ - mas morn; That comes on Christ - mas morn. ___

40

GOD REST YE MERRY, GENTLEMEN

TRADITIONAL

40640

THE FIRST NOEL

TRADITIONAL

1. The First No - el the an - gel did
2. They looked up and saw a
3. This star drew nigh to the north -
4. Then en - tered in those wise men

say Was to cer - tain poor shep - herds in fields as they
star Shin - ing in the east be - yond them
west, O'er Beth - le - hem it took its
three, Fell rev - 'rent - ly up - on their

lay, In fields where they lay keep - ing their
far And to the earth it gave great
rest And there it did both stop and
knees And of - fered there in His pre -

GOOD CHRISTIAN MEN, REJOICE

GERMAN TRADITIONAL

GOOD KING WENCESLAS

Moderato

TRADITIONAL

(Chorus) 1. Good King Wen-ces-las looked out On the feast of Steph-en When the snow lay 'round a-bout, Deep and crisp and e-ven. Bright-ly shone the moon that night, Though the frost was cru-el, When a poor man came in sight, Gath-'ring win-ter fu - el.

2

"Hither, page, and stand by me,
If thou know'st it, telling,
Yonder peasant, who is he,
Where and what his dwelling?"
"Sire, he lives a good league hence,
Underneath the mountain,
Right against the forest fence
By Saint Agnes' fountain."

3

"Bring me flesh and bring me wine,
Bring me pine logs hither.
Thou and I will see him dine
When we bear them thither."
Page and Monarch, forth they went,
Forth they went together
Through the rude winds' wild lament
And the bitter weather.

4

"Sire, the night is darker now
And the wind blows stronger.
Fails my heart, I know not how,
I can go not longer."
"Mark my footsteps, my good page,
Tread thou in them boldly.
Thou shall find the winter's rage
Freeze thy blood less coldly."

5

In his master's steps he trod
Where the snow lay dinted.
Heat was in the very sod
Which the saint had printed.
Therefore, Christian men be sure,
Wealth or rank possessing,
Ye who now will bless the poor
Shall yourselves find blessing.

HARK! THE HERALD ANGELS SING

CHAS. WESLEY
FELIX MENDELSSOHN

HERE WE COME A-WASSAILING

TRADITIONAL
ENGLISH

1. Here we come a-was-sail-ing A-mong the leaves so green,—

Here we come a-wan-der-ing, So fair to be seen:

CHORUS

Love and joy come to you, And to you your was-sail too, And God

bless you, and send you a hap-py new year.—

2. We are not daily beggars
   That beg from door to door,
   But we are neighbours' children
   Whom you have seen before:

3. We have got a little purse
   Of stretching leather skin;
   We want a little money
   To line it well within:

4. God bless the master of this house,
   Likewise the mistress too;
   And all the little children
   That round the table go:

THE CHIPMUNK SONG

(Christmas, Don't Be Late)

By ROSS BAGDASARIAN

49

A HOLLY JOLLY CHRISTMAS

By
JOHNNY MARKS

Moderately Bright With A Happy Feeling

Have A HOL-LY JOL-LY CHRIST-MAS, it's the best time of the year.__ I. don't know if there'll be snow but have a cup of cheer.__ Have A HOL-LY JOL-LY CHRIST-MAS, and when you walk down the street__ Say hel-lo to friends you know and ev-'ry-one you

(There's No Place Like)
HOME FOR THE HOLIDAYS

Words by AL STILLMAN
Music by ROBERT ALLEN

Moderato, Happily With Feeling

Oh, there's no place like HOME FOR THE HOL-I-DAYS __ 'cause no mat-ter how

far a-way you roam When you pine for the sun-shine of a friend-ly gaze__

for the hol-i-days you can't beat home, sweet home. I met a man who lives in

Ten-nes-see and he was head-in' for Penn-syl-van-ia and some home-made pump-kin pie.

I HEARD THE BELLS ON CHRISTMAS DAY

Words by
HENRY WADSWORTH LONGFELLOW
(Adapted by JOHNNY MARKS)
Music by JOHNNY MARKS

54

Will   To Men. I thought, as now this day had come, The
Will   To Men." Then pealed the bells more loud and deep, "God

bel - fries of all Chris - ten - dom Had rung so long the un-
is not dead, nor doth He sleep, The wrong shall fail, The

1.
bro - ken song Of Peace On Earth, Good Will   To Men.
right pre - vail, With

2.
Peace On Earth, Good Will   To Men."   *8va*

rit.

I SAW THREE SHIPS

Moderato

OLD ENGLISH MELODY

1. I saw three ships come sail-ing in On Christ-mas day, on Christ-mas day; I
2. And what was in those ships, all three, On Christ-mas day, on Christ-mas day? And
3. The Vir-gin Ma-ry and Christ were there, On Christ-mas day, on Christ-mas day; The

saw three ships come sail ing in On Christ-mas day in the morn - ing.
what was in those ships, all three, On Christ-mas day in the morn - ing?
Vir- gin Ma-ry and Christ were there, On Christ-mas day in the morn - ing.

IT CAME UPON THE MIDNIGHT CLEAR

Rev. E.H. SEARS
R. S. WILLIS

57

I Want To Wish You A Merry Christmas

Words and Music by
SAMMY KAYE

Slowly With Sincerity

I WANT TO WISH YOU___ A MER-RY CHRIST-MAS,___ A MER-RY

CHRIST-MAS___ to you.___ May your ev-'ry dream___

___ and ev-'ry hope___ and ev-'ry prayer___ come

I'LL BE HOME FOR CHRISTMAS

By KIM GANNON, WALTER KENT
and BUCK RAM

It's Christmas Time All Over The World

By HUGH MARTIN

64

JINGLE BELLS

By J. PIERPONT

Dash - ing through the snow in a one - horse o - pen sleigh,
Now the ground is white, go it while you're young.

O'er the fields we go, laugh - ing all the way.
Take the girls to - night and sing this sleigh - ing song. Just

sleigh! _____ Jin - gle bells, jin - gle bells, jin - gle all the way!

Oh, what fun it is to ride in a one-horse o - pen sleigh! one - horse

Optional
o - pen sleigh! _____

mp dim.

fp

p

JOY TO THE WORLD

Rev. ISAAC WATTS
G. F. HANDEL

JINGLE JINGLE JINGLE

By
JOHNNY MARKS

JOLLY OLD SAINT NICHOLAS

TRADITIONAL

JOY TO THE WORLD
(Religious Version)

Words and Music by
HOYT AXTON

Moderate Gospel Rock

1. Je-re-mi-ah was a pro-phet,   Mo-ses was a pro-phet
rea-son to be Chris-tian   is   just   as   plain   as
lost out on life's high-way   and you have no place to

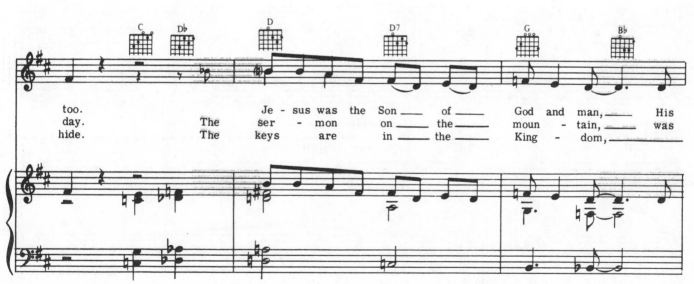

too.   Je-sus was the Son __ of __ God and man, __ His
day.   The ser-mon   on __ the __ moun-tain, __ was
hide.   The keys are   in __ the __ King-dom, __

40640

3. When you're

Coda

Joy To The World. All _____ the boys and girls.

Joy to the chil-dren of ____ Gal-i-lee, Joy to you and me. ____

Repeat and fade

LET IT SNOW! LET IT SNOW! LET IT SNOW!

Lyric by SAMMY CAHN
Music by JULE STYNE

LET THERE BE PEACE ON EARTH
(Let It Begin With Me)

By
SY MILLER and
JILL JACKSON

80

LITTLE DONKEY

Words and Music by
ERIC BOSWELL

LET'S HAVE AN OLD FASHIONED CHRISTMAS

(Song)

Lyric by LARRY CONLEY
Music by JOE SOLOMON

THE LITTLE DRUMMER BOY

Words and Music by
KATHERINE DAVIS,
HENRY ONORATI
and HARRY SIMEONE

86

on my drum.

Mar - y nod - ded pa - rum pum pum pum, _____

The Ox and Lamb Kept time pa - rum pum pum pum. _____

I played my drum for Him pa - rum pum pum pum, _____

I played my best for Him pa-rum pum pum pum rum pum pum pum

rum pum pum pum. ———

Then He smiled at me pa - rum pum pum pum ———

me and my drum. ———

89

MARY'S LITTLE BOY

Words and Music by
MASSIE PATTERSON and
SAMMY HEYWARD

THE MOST WONDERFUL DAY OF THE YEAR

By
JOHNNY MARKS

Refrain – Lightly

A pack-ful of toys means a sack-ful of joys for mil-lions of girls and for mil-lions of boys when Christ-mas Day is here_____ THE MOST WON-DER-FUL DAY OF THE YEAR!_____

A Jack in the box waits for chil-dren to shout, "Wake up, don't you know that it's time to come out!" When
It won't seem like Christ-mas till Dad gets his tie, "It's just what I want-ed" is his year-ly cry!

Christ-mas Day is here THE MOST WON-DER-FUL DAY OF THE

YEAR! Toys ga - lore scat - tered
Spir - its gay ev - 'ry -

on the floor. There's no room for
one will say Hap - py hol - i -

more And it's all be - cause of San - ta Claus! A
day And the best to you the whole year through. An

mp

94

scoot - er for Jim - my, a dol - ly for Sue, The kind that will e - ven say
e - lec - tric train hid - den high on a shelf that Dad - dy gives Da - vid but

"How do ya do!" When Christ - mas Day is here_____ THE MOST
then runs him - self.

1. WON - DER - FUL DAY OF THE YEAR._____ A   2. WON - DER - FUL, WON - DER - FUL,

WON - DER - FUL, WON - DER - FUL, WON - DER - FUL DAY OF THE YEAR._____

MY FAVORITE THINGS

Words by OSCAR HAMMERSTEIN II
Music by RICHARD RODGERS

Girls in white dress-es with blue sat-in sash-es, Snow-flakes that stay on my nose and eye-lash-es, Sil-ver white win-ters that melt in-to springs, These are a few of my fa-vor-ite things. When the dog bites, When the bee stings,

When I'm feel-ing sad,_____ I

sim - ply re - mem - ber my fa - vor - ite things and

then I don't feel so bad._____

99

MISTER SANTA

Lyric and Music by
PAT BALLARD
A.S.C.A.P.

"The
Night
Before
Christmas"

THE NIGHT BEFORE CHRISTMAS SONG

Lyrics adapted by
JOHNNY MARKS
From Clement Moore's Poem
Music by JOHNNY MARKS

104

sleigh and eight ti - ny rein - deer. A lit - tle old dri - ver so live - ly and
stock - ings; then turned with a jerk. And lay - ing his fin - ger a - side of his

quick, I knew in a mo - ment it must be St. Nick. And more rap - id than
nose, then giv - ing a nod up the chim - ney he rose; But I heard him ex -

ea - gles his rein - deer all came, As he shout - ed, "On Dash - er" and
claim as he drove out of sight, "Mer - ry Christ - mas to all and to

2nd Chorus rit.

1.

each rein - deer's name. *(Spoken)* Look—Here comes Rudolph!
opt. *8va* *loco* And so

2.

all a Good Night!"

8va

a tempo

O CHRISTMAS TREE

Moderately

O Christ-mas tree, O Christ-mas tree, How beau-ti-ful and bright.__ O

Christ-mas tree, O Christ-mas tree, How beau-ti-ful and bright.__ The

sight of thee at Christ-mas tide Spreads hope and glad-ness far and wide. O

Christ-mas tree, O Christ-mas tree, How beau-ti-ful and bright.__

O COME, ALL YE FAITHFUL

(Adeste Fideles)

Trans. by F. OAKELEY
WARD'S "CANTUS DIVERSI"

O HOLY NIGHT

Andante

A. ADAM

O LITTLE TOWN OF BETHLEHEM

Rev. PHILLIPS BROOKS
L. H. REDNER

1. O lit-tle town of Beth-le-hem, How still we see thee lie A-
3. (How) si-lent-ly, how si-lent-ly, The won-drous gift is giv-en! So

bove thy deep and dream-less sleep The si-lent stars go by, Yet, in thy dark streets
God im-parts to hu-man hearts The bless-ings of His heav-en. No ear may hear His

shin-eth The ev-er-last-ing light: The hopes and fears of all the years Are
com-ing; But in this world of sin, Where meek souls will re-ceive Him, still the

O COME, O COME IMMANUEL

Andante

FRENCH TRADITIONAL

1. O come, O come Im-man - u - el, And ran-som captive Is - ra - el, That mourns in lone-ly ex - ile here Un-til the Son of God ____ ap - pear.

2. O come, Thou key of Dav - id, come And o-pen wide our heav'n - ly home. Make safe the way that leads ____ on high And close the path to mis - er - y.

3. O come, O come, Thou Lord ____ of might, Who to Thy tribes on Si - nai's height, In an-cient times didst give ____ the law In cloud and ma-jes-ty ____ and awe.

Re - joice, re - joice! Im-man - u - el shall come to thee, O Is - ra - el!

PANIS ANGELICUS

CESAR FRANCK

ROCKIN' AROUND THE CHRISTMAS TREE

By
JOHNNY MARKS

Moderato With A Rock

ROCK-IN' A-ROUND THE CHRIST-MAS TREE. at the Christ-mas par-ty hop.

Mis-tle-toe hung where you can see ev-'ry cou-ple tries to stop.

ROCK-IN' A-ROUND THE CHRIST-MAS TREE,. let the Christ-mas spir-it ring.

Lat-er we'll have some pun-kin pie and we'll do some car-ol-ing.

RUDOLPH THE RED-NOSED REINDEER

By
JOHNNY MARKS

118

SANTA, SANTA, SANTA CLAUS

By
SUNNY SKYLAR and
SAMMY KAYE

1.A - way up north in the ice and snow___ there's a
(2.On) Christ - mas eve he'll be on his way___ through the
(3.He's) got a top and a scoot - er too___ and he's

jol - ly old man that we all know, He's big and round and
snow - y white clouds in his big sleigh with bags of sweets and
got a big bike that's paint - ed blue,___ he's got a doll with

wears a   grin___   and   long white whis-kers   on his   chin.___
lot of   toys___   for   all good lit - tle   girls and   boys.___
yel - low   hair___   and   lots of things for   kids to   wear.__

Refrain

SAN - TA, SAN - TA, SAN - TA CLAUS, mom-my says you'll

soon be here, SAN - TA, SAN - TA, SAN - TA CLAUS,

1 & 2

I've been ver - y good this year. 2. On
3. He's good this year.__

THE SEVEN JOYS OF MARY

Moderato

OLD ENGLISH CAROL

1. The first good joy that Ma-ry had, It was the joy of one,___ To see the bless-ed
2. The next good joy that Ma-ry had, It was the joy of two,___ To see her own son,
3. The next good joy that Ma-ry had, It was the joy of three,___ To see her own son,
4. The next good joy that Ma-ry had, It was the joy of four,___ To see her own son,
5. The next good joy that Ma-ry had, It was the joy of five,___ To see her own son,
6. The next good joy that Ma-ry had, It was the joy of six,___ To see her own son,
7. The next good joy that Ma-ry had, It was the joy of seven,___ To see her own son,

Je-sus Christ When He was first her Son.___ When He was first her Son,
Je-sus Christ___ Make the lame to go.___ ___ Make the lame to go,
Je-sus Christ___ Make the blind to see.___ ___ Make the blind to see, Good Lord, And
Je-sus Christ___ Read the bi-ble o'er.___ ___ Read the bi-ble o'er,
Je-sus Christ___ Raise the dead to life.___ ___ Raise the dead to life,
Je-sus Christ Up-on the cru-ci-fix.___ Up-on the cru-ci-fix,
Je-sus Christ A-scend-ing in to Heav'n. A-scend-ing in to Heav'n,

hap-py may we be.___ Praise Fa-ther, Son and Ho-ly Ghost To all e-ter-ni-ty!___

SHEPHERDS! SHAKE OFF YOUR DROWSY SLEEP

TRADITIONAL
Besancon Carol

1. Shep - herds! shake off your drow - sy sleep, Rise and leave your sil - ly
2. Hark! e - ven now the bells ring 'round, Lis - ten to their mer - ry
3. See how the flow'rs all burst a - new, Think - ing snow is sum - mer

sheep; An - gels from heav'n a - round loud sing - ing, Ti - dings of ___ great joy ___ are
sound; Hark! how the birds new songs are mock - ing, As ___ if win - ter's chains were
dew; See how the stars a - fresh are glow - ing, All their bright - est beams ___ be -

bring - ing.
break - ing. Shep-herds! the cho - rus come and swell! Sing No - el, O sing ___ No - el!
stow - ing.

4. Cometh at length the age of peace,
   Strife and sorrow now shall cease;
   Prophets foretold the wondrous story
   Of this heav'n-born Prince of Glory.

5. Shepherds! then up and quick away,
   Seek the Babe ere break of day;
   He is the hope of ev'ry nation,
   All in Him shall find salvation.

123

SILENT NIGHT! HOLY NIGHT!

FRANZ GRUBER
JOSEPH MOHR

124

SILVER AND GOLD

By
JOHNNY MARKS

Slowly And Expressively

SIL - VER AND GOLD,   SIL - VER AND GOLD,   Ev - 'ry - one

wish - es for SIL - VER AND GOLD,   How   do you   meas - ure   its

worth?_____   Just   by the   pleas - ure   it   gives here   on

earth. SIL - VER AND GOLD, SIL - VER AND GOLD,

Mean so much more when I see _____ SIL - VER AND

GOLD dec - o - ra - tions _____ on ev - 'ry Christ - mas

1. tree. _____ 2. tree. _____

SILVER BELLS

Words and Music by
JAY LIVINGSTON
and RAY EVANS

Voice – Brightly

Moderato

Christ - mas makes you feel e - mo - tion - al. It may bring par - ties or thoughts de - vo - tion - al. What - ev - er hap - pens or what may be, Here is what Christ - mas time means to me.

Refrain – Moderato and Tenderly

Cit - y side - walks, bus - y side - walks dressed in hol - i - day style. In the
street lights, ev - en stop lights, blink a bright red and green, As the

129

SLEEP, HOLY BABE

Rev. EDWARD CASWELL
J.B. DYKES

SNOWFALL

Lyrics by RUTH THORNHILL
Music by CLAUDE THORNHILL

SLEIGH RIDE

Words by MITCHELL PARISH
Music by LEROY ANDERSON

40640

THE STAR CAROL

Old country bagpipers came into Naples during the Christmas season to sing and play this song. Traditionally, two tenors sang, and a clarinetist took over between verses. The Italian bagpipe has a lower pitch than that of its Scottish cousin, and the bass is not the Scottish droning monotone but has notes, which gives harmony to the instrument. The new poetry by Peter Seeger is not a translation of the original lyrics, but was written in the spirit and flavor of the old Neapolitan carol.

Traditional Neapolitan Carol
English Lyric and Music Adaptation by
PETER SEEGER

In pastoral style (♩=152)

1. 'Twas on a night like this,____ A lit-tle babe__ was born;____
A-bove them shone a star,____ A star__ so won-d'rous light;____

____ The shep-herds gath-ered 'round ____ To__ guard Him till the dawn. A
____ Nev-er since 'in all these years Have we seen one half so bright.

CHORUS

Shin-ing so tru-ly, shin-ing so bright-ly, Guid-ing their foot-steps from a-far____ It led them

through the night,__ A path to love and broth-er-hood__ By__ fol-low-ing its light.____

2. Oh, come with us tonight,
   And join us on our way;
For we have found that star once more
To greet a better day.
For though throughout our land
Men search the skies in vain,
Yet turn their glance within their hearts
They would find this star again.

CHORUS
Shining so truly, shining so brightly,
Guiding our footsteps from afar
It leads us through the night,
A path to love and brotherhood
By following its light.

STAR OF THE EAST

Moderato

GEORGE COOPER
AMANDA KENNEDY

Star of the East, O Beth - le - hem's star, Guid - ing us on to
Star of the East, un - dimmed by each cloud, What though the storms of

heav - en a - far, Sor - row and grief are lulled by thy light, Thou
grief gath - er loud? Faith - ful and pure thy rays beam to save, Still

hope of each mor - tal in death's lone - ly night.
bright o'er the cra - dle and bright o'er the grave. Fear - less and tran - quil, we

look up to thee, Know - ing thou beam'st through e - ter - ni - ty.

STAR OF HOPE

By PHIL BOUTELJE and
HARRY TOBIAS
From a Theme by
E. WALDTEUFEL

Moderato

softly

Mist - y clouds veil the sky,

(Melody in L.H.)

But one star is shin - ing.

142

long wear - y years,_____ You're the star of faith STAR OF HOPE from heav - en a - bove _____ Let each beam guide our dreams lead - ing to hope and love._____ love._____

rall.

144

TOYLAND
"Jeunesse"

Lyric by GLEN MAC DONOUGH
Music by VICTOR HERBERT
French version by EMELIA RENAUD

Toy - land! Toy - land! Lit - tle girl and boy - land,
Ten - dres an - nées, pe-tits gar-çons et fil - les,

pp dolcissimo

While you dwell with - in it___ You are ev - er hap - py then.
Pro - fi - tez du bon-heur___ que vous of - fre le prin - temps,

Child - hood's Joy - land, Mys - tic mer - ry Toy - land!
Soy - ez heu - reux de___ cet - te jeu - nes - se,

Once you pass its bor-ders you can ne'er re-turn a - gain.___ When gain.___
Quand on en fran-chit le seuil, on n'y peut plus re - ve - nir.___ Quand nir.___

rit.   *rit.*   *pp*

147

THAT CHRISTMAS FEELING

Words by JOHNNY BURKE
Music by JIMMY VAN HEUSEN

THE TWELVE DAYS OF CHRISTMAS

TRADITIONAL

* This section to be played for verses 6 through 12 - "On the sixth day", "On the seventh day", etc.

** This portion of this measure to be played on each repeat of the section with the indicated "gift", and then all the "gifts" repeated in reverse order as often as necessary, thus: - - -

6. Six geese a-laying
7. Seven swans a-swimming
8. Eight maids a-milking
9. Nine ladies dancing
10. Ten lords a-leaping
11. 'Leven pipers piping
12. Twelve drummers drumming

5. Five gold rings
4. Four calling birds
3. Three French hens
2. Two turtle doves, and a partridge, etc.

WE NEED A LITTLE CHRISTMAS

Music and Lyric by
JERRY HERMAN

WE THREE KINGS OF ORIENT ARE

Rev. J. H. HOPKINS
TRADITIONAL

O_____ star of won-der, star of night, Star with roy-al beau-ty bright, West-ward lead-ing, still pro-ceed-ing, Guide us to thy Per-fect Light.

WE WISH YOU A MERRY CHRISTMAS

ENGLISH

We wish you a mer-ry Christ-mas, We wish you a mer-ry Christ-mas, We wish you a mer-ry Christ-mas and a hap-py New Year!___ Good tid-ings to you, where-ev-er you

WHAT CHILD IS THIS?

ENGLISH ("GREENSLEEVES")

What Child is this, Who laid to rest on
lies He in such mean es - tate, Where
bring Him in - cense, gold and myrrh, come

Mar - y's lap is sleep - ing? Whom
ox and ass are feed - ing? Good
peas - ant, king to own Him. The

While Shepherds Watched Their Flock By Night

NAHUM TATE
OLD ENGLISH MELODY

163

WHEN SANTA CLAUS GETS YOUR LETTER

By
JOHNNY MARKS

164

UP ON THE HOUSE TOP

By
B. R. HANBY

WINDS THROUGH THE OLIVE TREES

TRADITIONAL